Violin Exam Pieces

ABRSM Grade 4

Selected from the 2016–2019 syllabus

Name

D0230848

Date of exam

Contents

page

LIST A

1 **Anon.** The New Round O, arr. Edward Huws Jones   2

2 **Antonio Vivaldi** Allegro: fifth movement from Sonata in G, RV 25   3

3 **Joseph Haydn** Allegretto: second movement from Symphony No. 101 in D, 'The Clock',   4
   Hob. I/101, arr. Watson Forbes

LIST B

1 **Charles Dancla** Mazurka: No. 11 from *Petite école de la mélodie*, Op. 123, Book 2   6

2 **Ole Bull** Sæterjentens Søndag, arr. Johan Svendsen   8

3 **Franz Schubert** Entr'acte No. 3: No. 5 from *Rosamunde*, D. 797, arr. David Blackwell 10

LIST C

1 **Paul Desmond** Take Five, arr. Edward Huws Jones   12

2 **Kurt Weill** and **Bertolt Brecht** Tango–Ballade: No. 5 from *Sieben Stücke nach der* 14
   Dreigroschenoper, arr. Stefan Frenkel

3 **Timothy Salter** Daydream   16

Violin consultant: Philippa Bunting
Footnotes: Edward Huws Jones (EHJ), Richard Jones (RJ) and Anthony Burton

Other pieces for Grade 4

LIST A

4 **Handel** Presto (from Sonata for Flute, Op. 1 No. 9). *Sheila M. Nelson's Baroque Violinist* (Boosey & Hawkes)

5 **D. Ortiz** Recercada (*violin melody*). *The Early Music Fiddler*, arr. Huws Jones (Boosey & Hawkes)

6 **Purcell** Rondeau (from *Abdelazer*). *Superpieces*, arr. Cohen (Faber) or *The Best of Grade 4 Violin* (Faber)

LIST B

4 **Gabriel-Marie** La Cinquantaine. *The Best of Grade 4 Violin* (Faber)

5 **F. Küchler** Allegro moderato: 1st movt from Concertino in D, Op. 12 (Bosworth)

6 **Rieding** Marcia, Op. 44 (Bärenreiter)

LIST C

4 **Daphne Baker** Harlequin (Spartan Press)

5 **Scott Skinner** MacPherson's Blade. *Alastair Hardie's Compliments to 'The King'* (Hardie Press)

6 **Ros Stephen** Milonga pampeana. No. 11 from *Argentinian Tango and Folk Tunes for Violin* (Schott)

First published in 2015 by ABRSM (Publishing) Ltd,
a wholly owned subsidiary of ABRSM, 24 Portland
Place, London W1B 1LU, United Kingdom
© 2015 by The Associated Board of the Royal
Schools of Music

Music origination by Andrew Jones
Cover by Kate Benjamin & Andy Potts
Printed in England by Caligraving Ltd, Thetford,
Norfolk, on materials from sustainable sources.
Reprinted in 2016.

The New Round O

Arranged by Edward Huws Jones

Anon.

D.C. al Fine

John Playford's *The English Dancing Master* was first published in 1651, immediately after the English Civil War, and continued to be reprinted by his son Henry and others well into the 18th century. But the contents of the collection were constantly changing along with musical fashions, and this tune first appeared in 1703. The 'round o' in the title refers to the rondo form, with contrasting episodes (the passages in third position in this arrangement) sandwiched between appearances of the main theme. The piece needs a lively two-in-a-bar feel. EHJ

Allegro

Fifth movement from Sonata in G, RV 25

A:2

Edited by and continuo
realization by Richard Jones

Antonio Vivaldi
(1678–1741)

The Sonata in G (RV 25), from which this Allegro is selected, is the third of four sonatas that Vivaldi composed in 1716–17 for Johann Georg Pisendel, a young German virtuoso who lived in Venice around that time and became a friend and pupil of the composer.

The G major Sonata is a *sonata da camera* (chamber sonata) – its seven movements are all based on dance rhythms and constructed in binary form with repeats. The fifth movement, reproduced here, is written in the style of a *giga* (that is, an Italian gigue). The tempo and dynamic marks are editorial additions, as is the continuo realization (the upper stave of the keyboard part) and the sharp to the violin C in b. 11. RJ

Source: Dresden, Sächsische Landesbibliothek, Mus. 2389-R-10.

A:3

Allegretto

Second movement from Symphony No. 101 in D, 'The Clock', Hob. I/101

Arranged by Watson Forbes

Joseph Haydn
(1732–1809)

Joseph Haydn wrote the last 12 of his more than 100 symphonies for two highly successful extended visits to London in the 1790s, before he returned to his native Austria to live in semi-retirement. His Symphony No. 101 was first performed at the Hanover Square Rooms in London in March 1794. Its second movement was immediately repeated by public demand (concert manners were different in those days). Originally written as an Andante in 2/4 time, it has a principal melody for the first violins with an accompaniment on bassoons and pizzicato strings that imitates the ticking of a clock. When the movement was published in a piano arrangement in Vienna in 1798, the publisher gave it the title of 'The Clock', and during the 19th century the nickname came to be applied to the whole symphony. The first section of the movement is adapted here for violin and piano.

Mazurka

No. 11 from *Petite école de la mélodie*, Op. 123, Book 2

Edited by Richard Jones

Charles Dancla
(1817–1907)

Petite école de la mélodie   Little School of Melody

Charles Dancla was a French violinist, teacher and composer, who studied at the Paris Conservatoire (1828–40), where he taught the violin from 1855, becoming a professor in 1860.

The mazurka, a Polish folk-dance in triple time, spread throughout Europe, becoming very popular as a drawing-room dance in the 1830s and 1840s. Dancla's A minor mazurka melody alternates with a contrasting dance tune in the submediant, F major (bb. 17–32). An abridged variant of this second tune returns as a coda in the tonic major, A (bb. 50–8). The optional consecutive down-bows in the last three bars are to be played 'at the heel' (*du talon*) and with a 'very light and well-lifted bow' (*bien léger et bien enlevé*). 'Sim.', short for *simile*, in bb. 19 and 52 is an editorial addition, as is the *p* in the piano part at b. 33 and *f* in the violin part at b. 50. At bb. 17 and 50, *sautillé*, a form of spiccato bowing, literally means 'skipped', but this technique is not expected in the exam and regular staccato is acceptable. RJ

Source: *Petite école de la mélodie. 12 petites pièces pour le violon avec accomp^t. de piano*, Op. 123 (Paris, 1868), 2e Livre.

B:2

Sæterjentens Søndag

Arranged by Johan Svendsen

Ole Bull
(1810–80)

Sæterjentens Søndag The Shepherd-girl's Sunday

Ole Bull was one of the most famous violinists of the 19th century, and also a composer and conductor; his concert tours played a major role in making the music of his native Norway known throughout the world. Bull's compositions contain many melodies borrowed from, or written in imitation of, Norwegian folk music. One invented tune is the violin melody of *Sæterjentens Søndag* (*The Shepherd-girl's Sunday*) – alternatively known as *Solitude sur la montagne* (*Solitude on the Mountain*) – which was also turned into a well-known song, 'På solen jeg ser' ('I gaze upon the sun'). The accompaniment, for string orchestra or piano, was written by a friend of Bull, the Danish composer, violinist and conductor Johan Svendsen.

Violin Exam Pieces

ABRSM Grade 4

Selected from the 2016–2019 syllabus

Piano accompaniment

Contents

    page

LIST A

1 **Anon.** The New Round O, arr. Edward Huws Jones   2

2 **Antonio Vivaldi** Allegro: fifth movement from Sonata in G, RV 25   4

3 **Joseph Haydn** Allegretto: second movement from Symphony No. 101 in D, 'The Clock',   6
Hob. I/101, arr. Watson Forbes

LIST B

1 **Charles Dancla** Mazurka: No. 11 from *Petite école de la mélodie*, Op. 123, Book 2   9

2 **Ole Bull** Sæterjentens Søndag, arr. Johan Svendsen   12

3 **Franz Schubert** Entr'acte No. 3: No. 5 from *Rosamunde*, D. 797, arr. David Blackwell   14

LIST C

1 **Paul Desmond** Take Five, arr. Edward Huws Jones   17

2 **Kurt Weill** and **Bertolt Brecht** Tango–Ballade: No. 5 from *Sieben Stücke nach der*   22
Dreigroschenoper, arr. Stefan Frenkel

3 **Timothy Salter** Daydream   20

The order of pieces has been changed in the score to facilitate page turns.

Violin consultant: Philippa Bunting
Footnotes: Edward Huws Jones (EHJ), Richard Jones (RJ) and Anthony Burton

The pieces in this album have been taken from a variety of different sources. Where appropriate, they have been checked with original source material and edited to help the player when preparing for performance. The fingering and bowing have been amended where necessary to ensure a consistent approach within the album. Ornament realizations have been added, as have metronome marks shown within square brackets. Details of other editorial amendments or suggestions are given in the footnotes. Fingering, bowing and all editorial additions are for guidance only; they are not comprehensive or obligatory.

ABRSM Violin Exams: requirements

Pieces
In the exam, candidates must play three pieces, one chosen from each of the three syllabus lists (A, B and C). Candidates are free to choose from the pieces printed in this album and/or from the other pieces set for the grade: a full list is given in the violin part with this score as well as in the 2016–2019 Bowed Strings syllabus.

Scales and arpeggios
Sight-reading   } Full details are available online at www.abrsm.org/violin4
Aural tests

First published in 2015 by ABRSM (Publishing) Ltd, a wholly owned subsidiary of ABRSM, 24 Portland Place, London W1B 1LU, United Kingdom © 2015 by The Associated Board of the Royal Schools of Music

Music origination by Andrew Jones Cover by Kate Benjamin & Andy Potts Printed in England by Caligraving Ltd, Thetford, Norfolk, on materials from sustainable sources. Reprinted in 2016.

The New Round O

Arranged by Edward Huws Jones

Anon.

John Playford's *The English Dancing Master* was first published in 1651, immediately after the English Civil War, and continued to be reprinted by his son Henry and others well into the 18th century. But the contents of the collection were constantly changing along with musical fashions, and this tune first appeared in 1703. The 'round o' in the title refers to the rondo form, with contrasting episodes (the passages in third position in this arrangement) sandwiched between appearances of the main theme. The piece needs a lively two-in-a-bar feel. EHJ

D.C. al Fine

Allegro

Fifth movement from Sonata in G, RV 25

Edited by and continuo
realization by Richard Jones

Antonio Vivaldi
(1678–1741)

The Sonata in G (RV 25), from which this Allegro is selected, is the third of four sonatas that Vivaldi composed in 1716–17 for Johann Georg Pisendel, a young German virtuoso who lived in Venice around that time and became a friend and pupil of the composer.

The G major Sonata is a *sonata da camera* (chamber sonata) – its seven movements are all based on dance rhythms and constructed in binary form with repeats. The fifth movement, reproduced here, is written in the style of a *giga* (that is, an Italian gigue). The tempo and dynamic marks are editorial additions, as is the continuo realization (the upper stave of the keyboard part) and the sharp to the violin C in b. 11. RJ

Source: Dresden, Sächsische Landesbibliothek, Mus. 2389-R-10.

Allegretto

Second movement from Symphony No. 101 in D, 'The Clock', Hob. I/101

Arranged by Watson Forbes

Joseph Haydn
(1732–1809)

Joseph Haydn wrote the last 12 of his more than 100 symphonies for two highly successful extended visits to London in the 1790s, before he returned to his native Austria to live in semi-retirement. His Symphony No. 101 was first performed at the Hanover Square Rooms in London in March 1794. Its second movement was immediately repeated by public demand (concert manners were different in those days). Originally written as an Andante in 2/4 time, it has a principal melody for the first violins with an accompaniment on bassoons and pizzicato strings that imitates the ticking of a clock. When the movement was published in a piano arrangement in Vienna in 1798, the publisher gave it the title of 'The Clock', and during the 19th century the nickname came to be applied to the whole symphony. The first section of the movement is adapted here for violin and piano.

AB 3782

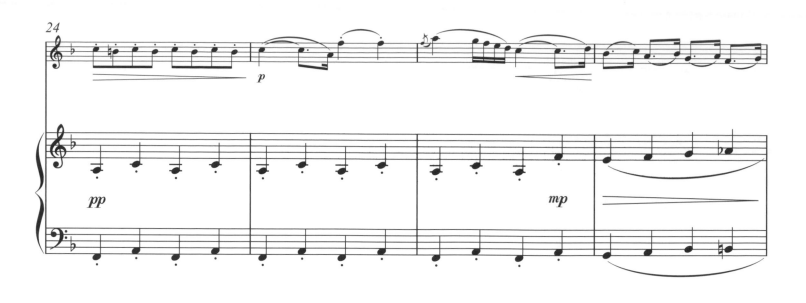

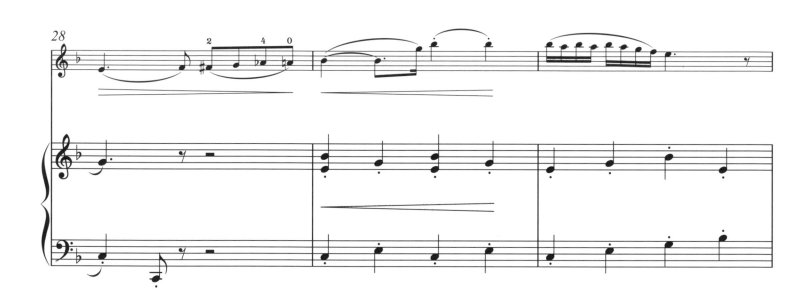

Mazurka

No. 11 from *Petite école de la mélodie*, Op. 123, Book 2

B:1

Edited by Richard Jones

Charles Dancla
(1817–1907)

Petite école de la mélodie   Little School of Melody

Charles Dancla was a French violinist, teacher and composer, who studied at the Paris Conservatoire (1828–40), where he taught the violin from 1855, becoming a professor in 1860.

The mazurka, a Polish folk-dance in triple time, spread throughout Europe, becoming very popular as a drawing-room dance in the 1830s and 1840s. Dancla's A minor mazurka melody alternates with a contrasting dance tune in the submediant, F major (bb. 17–32). An abridged variant of this second tune returns as a coda in the tonic major, A (bb. 50–8). The optional consecutive down-bows in the last three bars are to be played 'at the heel' (*du talon*) and with a 'very light and well-lifted bow' (*bien léger et bien enlevé*). 'Sim.', short for *simile*, in bb. 19 and 52 is an editorial addition, as is the ***p*** in the piano part at b. 33 and ***f*** in the violin part at b. 50. At bb. 17 and 50, *sautillé*, a form of spiccato bowing, literally means 'skipped', but this technique is not expected in the exam and regular staccato is acceptable. RJ

Source: *Petite école de la mélodie. 12 petites pièces pour le violon avec accomp¹. de piano*, Op. 123 (Paris, 1868), 2ᵉ Livre.

B:2

Sæterjentens Søndag

Arranged by Johan Svendsen

Ole Bull
(1810–80)

Sæterjentens Søndag   The Shepherd-girl's Sunday

Ole Bull was one of the most famous violinists of the 19th century, and also a composer and conductor; his concert tours played a major role in making the music of his native Norway known throughout the world. Bull's compositions contain many melodies borrowed from, or written in imitation of, Norwegian folk music. One invented tune is the violin melody of *Sæterjentens Søndag* (*The Shepherd-girl's Sunday*) – alternatively known as *Solitude sur la montagne* (*Solitude on the Mountain*) – which was also turned into a well-known song, 'På solen jeg ser' ('I gaze upon the sun'). The accompaniment, for string orchestra or piano, was written by a friend of Bull, the Danish composer, violinist and conductor Johan Svendsen.

Entr'acte No. 3

No. 5 from *Rosamunde*, D. 797

Arranged by David Blackwell

Franz Schubert
(1797–1828)

Franz Schubert struggled hard during his short lifetime to establish himself in the musical life of his native Vienna, and especially in its theatres. His last attempt was in 1823, with his incidental music for a pastoral play called *Rosamunde, Fürstin von Zypern* (Rosamunde, Princess of Cyprus) by Helmina von Chézy. This well-known Entr'acte served as a prelude to the final act of the play, set in an idyllic valley where the heroine Rosamunde is tending a flock of sheep. In the original version, the main section, in which the first violins take the melodic lead, alternates with two episodes in which the melody is entrusted to woodwind instruments; this arrangement includes the first of these episodes. Schubert must have been fond of the gentle main tune since he used it twice more, in a string quartet and a piano impromptu.

Minore

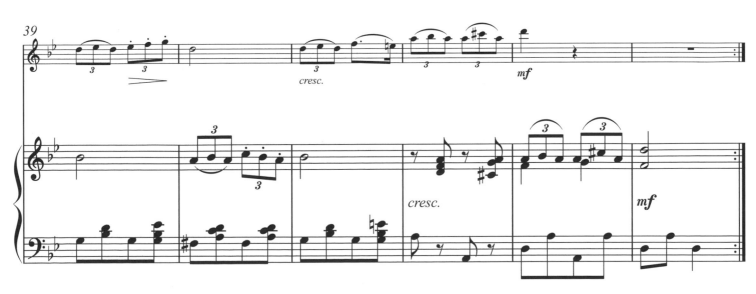

D.C. al Fine

Take Five

Arranged by Edward Huws Jones

Paul Desmond
(1924–77)

The Dave Brubeck Quartet was one of the most popular modern jazz groups of the 1950s and 60s, in its native USA and internationally. It specialized in pieces written in unusual metres for jazz, such as 7/4 and 11/4. Most of these were composed by the group's classically trained pianist and leader, Dave Brubeck, but the best known was written by the quartet's alto saxophonist Paul Desmond. This was 'Take Five', first released on the album *Time Out* in 1959 and later issued as a single, becoming the first jazz instrumental recording to sell a million copies. The title, a familiar instruction to take a five-minute break from work, is used in reference to the 5/4 metre of the piece. The piano maintains an ostinato pattern while the saxophone, or in this version the violin, plays the tune.

18

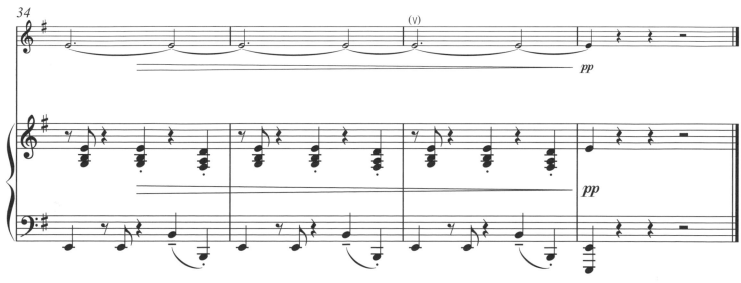

Daydream

Timothy Salter
born 1942

Timothy Salter is a composer, pianist and conductor, based in London, where for many years he taught composition and performance studies at the Royal College of Music. He wrote *Daydream* in June 2007 for *Spectrum for Violin*, ABRSM's album of 16 newly commissioned violin pieces. In his own note on it, he says: 'The direction "musing" gives the character of this piece, although a more openly lyrical few bars emerge in the middle. The pizzicati and staccato phrases afford a contrast with the smooth flow of the opening scalic idea. In the piano part, pedalling is at the performer's discretion except where specified.'

AB 3782

C:2

Tango–Ballade

No. 5 from *Sieben Stücke nach Der Dreigroschenoper*

Arranged by Stefan Frenkel

Kurt Weill (1900–50)
and Bertolt Brecht (1898–1956)

Sieben Stücke nach Der Dreigroschenoper   Seven Pieces after The Threepenny Opera

Kurt Weill was one of the leading composers in the field of musical theatre in the first half of the 20th century: first in his native Germany, where he produced a variety of innovative works; later in the USA, where he brought fresh ideas to the Broadway musical. His biggest success in the first phase of his career was with *Die Dreigroschenoper* ('The Threepenny Opera'), an early product of his partnership with the radical poet and playwright Bertolt Brecht, which was premiered in Berlin in 1928. The show is a free adaptation of John Gay's 1728 ballad opera *The Beggar's Opera*, which had been a hit in 18th-century London; it is set in the Soho district of London, amidst thieves and other low-life characters. Just as Gay had drawn on familiar ballads and folk dances for much of his score, so Weill wrote songs in the popular dance rhythms of the time, including this ballade in tango rhythm. The version here is from a suite of arrangements of pieces from *Die Dreigroschenoper* made by Stefan Frenkel, a Polish-born violinist who was a friend of Weill and a trusted interpreter of his music, and who also emigrated to the USA. Although the arranger's metronome mark is ♩ = 85, a more relaxed tempo of ♩ = c.76 would be acceptable in the exam.

24

B:3

Entr'acte No. 3

No. 5 from *Rosamunde*, D. 797

Arranged by David Blackwell

Franz Schubert
(1797–1828)

Franz Schubert struggled hard during his short lifetime to establish himself in the musical life of his native Vienna, and especially in its theatres. His last attempt was in 1823, with his incidental music for a pastoral play called *Rosamunde, Fürstin von Zypern* (Rosamunde, Princess of Cyprus) by Helmina von Chézy. This well-known Entr'acte served as a prelude to the final act of the play, set in an idyllic valley where the heroine Rosamunde is tending a flock of sheep. In the original version, the main section, in which the first violins take the melodic lead, alternates with two episodes in which the melody is entrusted to woodwind instruments; this arrangement includes the first of these episodes. Schubert must have been fond of the gentle main tune since he used it twice more, in a string quartet and a piano impromptu.

Minore

poco rit.

D.C. al Fine

C:1

Take Five

Arranged by Edward Huws Jones

Paul Desmond
(1924–77)

The Dave Brubeck Quartet was one of the most popular modern jazz groups of the 1950s and 60s, in its native USA and internationally. It specialized in pieces written in unusual metres for jazz, such as 7/4 and 11/4. Most of these were composed by the group's classically trained pianist and leader, Dave Brubeck, but the best known was written by the quartet's alto saxophonist Paul Desmond. This was 'Take Five', first released on the album *Time Out* in 1959 and later issued as a single, becoming the first jazz instrumental recording to sell a million copies. The title, a familiar instruction to take a five-minute break from work, is used in reference to the 5/4 metre of the piece. The piano maintains an ostinato pattern while the saxophone, or in this version the violin, plays the tune.

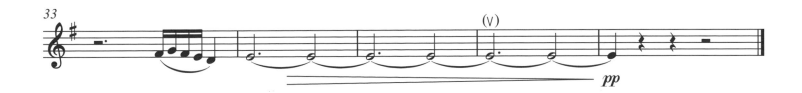

C:2

Tango–Ballade

No. 5 from *Sieben Stücke nach Der Dreigroschenoper*

Arranged by Stefan Frenkel

Kurt Weill (1900–50)
and Bertolt Brecht (1898–1956)

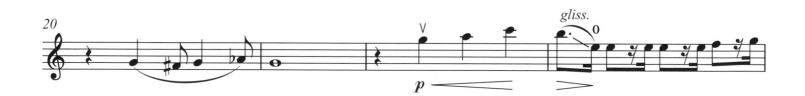

Sieben Stücke nach Der Dreigroschenoper   Seven Pieces after The Threepenny Opera

Kurt Weill was one of the leading composers in the field of musical theatre in the first half of the 20th century: first in his native Germany, where he produced a variety of innovative works; later in the USA, where he brought fresh ideas to the Broadway musical. His biggest success in the first phase of his career was with *Die Dreigroschenoper* ('The Threepenny Opera'), an early product of his partnership with the radical poet and playwright Bertolt Brecht, which was premiered in Berlin in 1928. The show is a free adaptation of John Gay's 1728 ballad opera *The Beggar's Opera*, which had been a hit in 18th-century London; it is set in the Soho district of London, amidst thieves and other low-life characters. Just as Gay had drawn on familiar ballads and folk dances for much of his score, so Weill wrote songs in the popular dance rhythms of the time, including this ballade in tango rhythm. The version here is from a suite of arrangements of pieces from *Die Dreigroschenoper* made by Stefan Frenkel, a Polish-born violinist who was a friend of Weill and a trusted interpreter of his music, and who also emigrated to the USA. Although the arranger's metronome mark is ♩ = 85, a more relaxed tempo of ♩ = *c.*76 would be acceptable in the exam.

Daydream

Timothy Salter
born 1942

Timothy Salter is a composer, pianist and conductor, based in London, where for many years he taught composition and performance studies at the Royal College of Music. He wrote *Daydream* in June 2007 for *Spectrum for Violin*, ABRSM's album of 16 newly commissioned violin pieces. In his own note on it, he says: 'The direction "musing" gives the character of this piece, although a more openly lyrical few bars emerge in the middle. The pizzicati and staccato phrases afford a contrast with the smooth flow of the opening scalic idea.'